Louis

rika Meza

M ry book

wren
&rook

This is my grandma.

She has white hair, lots of wrinkles, kind eyes and a big smile.

I love visiting my grandma,
it's always lots of fun.

We read together, play her piano,
we feed the birds in the garden and we
love looking through her big box of photos.

Some photos are in colour,
some are black and white,
and some are a funny brown
colour and look really old!

I like to pull out all the
photos from when Grandma
was little and line them up
next to photos of me.

"I remember when I was your age," says Grandma.

"You have curly hair just like me," I say, with a giggle.

"And the same cheeky smile," adds Grandma.

But recently, my grandma seems to be getting in a muddle. She doesn't always remember who the people in the pictures are.

I tell her I forget things all the time too. I sometimes forget how to tie my shoelaces, and Mum can never remember where she has put her car keys!

But when Grandma forgets, she says it makes her feel VERY frustrated.

Grandma has also started to put things in funny places.

She once left the television remote in the bathroom . . .

She put her cup of tea in the fridge . . .

She is always losing her glasses . . .

And, oh no! Where did she put her box of photos?

Grandma's house is starting to feel very different.

Mum explains that Grandma is living with something called dementia.

"Dementia changes the way she thinks and behaves, and can make her very forgetful and confused. It can happen when some people get older."

"I don't want Grandma to change," I say.

"Even though she is living with dementia, she hasn't stopped being the person we know and love." Mum takes my hands. "Grandma is still Grandma, she's just a little different now."

As time goes by, Grandma's memory
seems to be getting worse and worse.

lamp

plant

jug

Mum thinks of some ways we can help.
She says we must always talk to Grandma
about any changes we make around her,
as we don't want her to feel left out.

Grandma agrees that it would be useful
to label some of the items around
the house, so she doesn't forget what
they are and what they do.

"I'm using all my
favourite pens and
stickers!" I tell her.

cat

Roger
dad

lamp

phone

Even though Grandma is a bit different, we still read together,

we play her piano

and we feed the birds in the garden.

But where are Grandma's photos? I don't like to ask . . .

Grandma still loves telling me stories.

I remember when ...

I remember when ...

But sometimes, only a few minutes later, she tells me the same story again – even though I've just heard it!

She often calls me by the wrong name and acts a bit funny at times too.

It can give me the giggles, but it can also be quite embarrassing.

Mum says that maybe Grandma could do with more help at home.

I start to realise that Grandma has good days and she has bad days.

The neighbours still like to pop in for a cup of tea, but now Grandma has a special person, called a care worker, who comes to help her around the house or to take her to the shops.

Some days Grandma doesn't really like this, and she gets very flustered.

"Who is this person? Why is he here?" she asks. "I can do all of this on my own!"

It makes me sad to see Grandma like this.

"Why don't we just move in with Grandma?" I ask.

"That's a lovely idea, but we wouldn't be around enough," replies Mum. "She's got more help at home now so she'll soon feel more at ease."

"We'll still pop in," Mum adds. "Grandma loves to see your cheeky smile!"

Mum gives me a great big hug.

"Maybe there is something you can help me with," she says.
"Something that could really cheer up Grandma."

Mum takes me into her room and there on her bed are . . .

"**The photos**! I thought Grandma had lost them!"

"I agreed with Grandma that we would organise them and make her a memory book," says Mum, "full of all the special people and events throughout her life."

"I can label them like I did with all the things in her house!" I say. "Then she will always remember when the photos were taken, and who's who!"

"I think that's a great idea,"
says Mum, with a smile.

This is my grandma. We read together,

play her piano

and feed the birds in the garden.

"Now let's look through your new memory book, Grandma!"

"I remember when I was your age," says Grandma, turning the pages.

We look through the colour photos, the black and white ones, and the really old brown ones.

"Oh! Did you forget to fill the pages at the back?" asks Grandma.

"No, Grandma! That's for filling with all the memories we're STILL going to make!"

What is dementia?

As people get older, we can see things like wrinkles, greying hair, walking sticks or hearing aids. But there are some things we cannot see, like how someone's brain might be changing too.

Dementia is an illness that impacts a person's memory and how they think and feel. It will make things that they used to do every day, like cooking, cleaning or going to the shops, much more difficult to do by themselves.

Here are some other changes that you might notice:

- Forgetfulness – not remembering names, faces or places

- Confusion – muddling days of the week, getting lost or not being able to perform simple tasks any more

- Repetition – telling the same stories over and over, or asking questions that have just been answered

- Mood swings – going from happy emotions to sad or frustrated more quickly

Looking after you

Having a family member living with dementia can be difficult and may bring a whole range of new emotions for you too.

Some days can still be a lot of fun with them, but other days you may feel sad, angry, confused, embarrassed and maybe even worried.

Here are some things that can help you to feel better:

- Talk about your worries with someone you trust

- Share happy memories with friends and family members

- Ask a grown-up any questions you have about dementia

A person living with dementia might be acting differently, but always remember they still love you very much!

How you can help

When you see someone you love changing, it can be very difficult – but there are ways you and your family can help them at home:

- Leave notes with reminders about appointments or any visitors coming

- Label everyday objects to remind them what things are and how they work

- Label photographs to help them recognise who is who

- Create a photo album or memory box to encourage sharing memories and milestones

Sometimes, people living with dementia may need more help than their families can give, so they have to move to a special care home where they have carers and nurses ready to assist them.

No matter where they're living, encouraging their hobbies and interests is also very important, and there are lots you can try together.

- Singing

- Playing musical instruments

- Gardening

- Drawing

- Watching old movies and listening to music from their past

- Playing card games, board games and puzzles to help boost their memory

Sometimes these activities will be a little tiring for someone living with dementia, so just spending quiet time with them or chatting will help too.

The best way you can help someone living with dementia is to give them your time, patience, understanding and love.

In fondest memory of Beeble Bubble/Bubble/Granny B,
whose silly songs and piano playing are missed by many – L.G.

For Jude, one of the coolest grandmas I know – E.M.

First published in Great Britain in 2023
by Wren & Rook

Text copyright © Louise Gooding, 2023
Illustration copyright © Erika Meza, 2023
Design copyright © Hodder & Stoughton Ltd, 2023
All rights reserved.

The right of Louise Gooding and Erika Meza to be
identified as the author and illustrator respectively of this
Work has been asserted by them in accordance with the
Copyright, Designs & Patents Act 1988.

HB ISBN: 978 1 5263 6375 6
PB ISBN: 978 1 5263 6376 3
E-book ISBN: 978 1 5263 6377 0
10 9 8 7 6 5 4 3 2 1

FSC
MIX
Paper from
responsible sources
FSC® C104740
www.fsc.org

Wren & Rook
An imprint of Hachette Children's Group
Part of Hodder & Stoughton
Carmelite House
50 Victoria Embankment
London EC4Y 0DZ

An Hachette UK Company
www.hachette.co.uk
www.hachettechildrens.co.uk

Printed in China